# *Flower Drum Song*

## VOCAL SELECTION

Music by
### RICHARD RODGERS

Lyrics by
### OSCAR HAMMERSTEIN II

## CONTENTS

## WILLIAMSON MUSIC, INC.

Applications for performance of this work, whether legitimate, stock,
amateur, or foreign, should be addressed to:
RODGERS & HAMMERSTEIN LIBRARY
598 Madison Avenue
New York, NY 10022

118984

# Don't Marry Me

Words by
OSCAR HAMMERSTEIN II

Music by
RICHARD RODGERS

**Optional ending with Coda**

me. \_\_\_\_\_ me. Mar - ry a

dope, In - no - cent and ga - ga, Mar - ry a Khan,

Al - i or the A - ga. Mar - ry for mon - ey, or mar - ry for

free, But don't mar - ry me. \_\_\_\_\_

# Grant Avenue

Words by
**OSCAR HAMMERSTEIN II**

Music by
**RICHARD RODGERS**

# A Hundred Million Miracles

Words by
OSCAR HAMMERSTEIN II

Music by
RICHARD RODGERS

Tranquillo *(calmly)*

When a dark blue cur-tain is pinned by the stars, Pinned by the stars to the sky, Ev-'ry flow'r and tree is a treat to see, The air is ver-y clean and dry. Then a wind comes blow-ing the pins all a-way, Night is con-fused and up - set! The__ sky falls down like a clum-sy clown, The flow-ers and the trees get wet. Ver-y wet! A

hun-dred mil-lion mir-a-cles are happ-'ning ev-'ry

## Coda (*Slowly and tenderly*)

*(Uke tacet)* MEI LI: day! _____ My fa-ther says the sun will keep ris-ing

o-ver the east-ern hill. *(Uke tacet)* My fa-ther says he does-n't know why but

OTHERS: It will! ____ some-how or oth-er it will. _____

some-how or oth-er it will. _____

# I Enjoy Being A Girl

**Words by**
**OSCAR HAMMERSTEIN II**

**Music by**
**RICHARD RODGERS**

# Love, Look Away

Words by
OSCAR HAMMERSTEIN II

Music by
RICHARD RODGERS

Lyrics:

They say you "make the world go 'round," They say you "con-quer all."

Love, won't you please stop con-q'ring me? Take some-one your size, I'm small;— Too

small to fight a-gainst the odds, Too tired to chase ro-mance,

# Sunday

Words by
**OSCAR HAMMERSTEIN II**

Music by
**RICHARD RODGERS**

Now that we're going to be mar - ried, I keep im - ag - in - ing things, Things that can hap - pen to peo - ple___ When they are wear - ing gold rings: Be - ing to - geth - er each morn - ing,

Shar - ing our cof - fee and toast. That's on - ly one of the

pic - tures. Here's what I pic - ture most.

*poco rit.*

Refrain *(gracefully)*

Sun - day, sweet Sun - day, with noth - ing to

do, Laz - y and love - ly, my

# You Are Beautiful

Words by
**OSCAR HAMMERSTEIN II**

Music by
**RICHARD RODGERS**